D0247513

FOUR O'CLOCK FRIDAY

original poems by

JOHN FOSTER

OXFORD

Sch
80 002 425 838

Contents

OXFORD
UNIVERSITY PRESS
Great Clarendon Street, Oxford OX2 6DP

*Oxford University Press is a department of the University of Oxford.
It furthers the University's objective of excellence in research, scholarship, and education by publishing worldwide in*

*Oxford New York
Athens Auckland Bangkok Bogotá Buenos Aires Calcutta
Cape Town Chennai Dar es Salaam Delhi Florence Hong Kong Istanbul
Karachi Kuala Lumpur Madrid Melbourne Mexico City Mumbai Nairobi
Paris São Paulo Singapore Taipei Tokyo Toronto Warsaw*

with associated companies in Berlin Ibadan

Oxford is a registered trade mark of Oxford University Press in the UK and certain other countries

Copyright © John Foster 1991

The moral rights of the author have been asserted

*First published 1991
Reprinted 1992
Reprinted in paperback only 1994, 1995, 1996
Reprinted in paperback with new cover 1998 (twice), 1999*

All rights reserved. No part of this publication may be reproduced, stored in a retrieval system, or transmitted, in any form or by any means, without the prior permission in writting of Oxford University Press. Within the UK, exceptions are allowed in respect of any fair dealing for the purpose of research or private study, or criticism or review, as permitted under the Copyright, Designs, and Patents Act, 1988, or in the case of reprographic reproduction in accordance with the terms of licences issued by the Copyright Licensing Agency. Enquiries concerning reproduction outside these terms and in other countries sould be sent to the Rights Department, Oxford Unviersity Press, at the address above.

This book is sold subject to the condition that it shall not, by way of trade or otherwise, be lent, resold, hired out, or otherwise circulated without the publisher's prior consent in any form of binding or cover other than that in which it is published and without a similar condition including this condition being imposed on the subsequent purchaser.

British Library Cataloguing in Publication Data available

ISBN 0 19 276093 9

*Illustrated by Debbie Cook
Cover illustration by Nick Sharratt*

Printed in Hong Kong

The secrets box

These are the keys
That open the locks
Of the secrets box.

This is the secrets box
Where deep inside
The stories hide.

This is the girl
Who found the keys
That open the locks
Of the secrets box.

These are the stories
Of dragons and kings,
Of wizards and rings,
Of dancing and sighs,
Of sunshine and lies.

This is the girl
Who heard the stories
From inside
And laughed and cried.

Ten dancing dinosaurs

Ten dancing dinosaurs in a chorus line
One fell and split her skirt, then there were nine.

Nine dancing dinosaurs at a village fête
One was raffled as a prize, then there were eight.

Eight dancing dinosaurs on a pier in Devon
One fell overboard, then there were seven.

Seven dancing dinosaurs performing magic tricks
One did a vanishing act, then there were six.

Six dancing dinosaurs learning how to jive
One got twisted in a knot, then there were five.

Five dancing dinosaurs gyrating on the floor
One crashed through the floorboards, then there were four.

Four dancing dinosaurs waltzing in the sea
A mermaid kidnapped one, then there were three.

Three dancing dinosaurs head-banging in a zoo
One knocked himself out, then there were two.

Two dancing dinosaurs rocking round the sun
One collapsed from sunstroke, then there was one.

One dancing dinosaur hijacked a plane,
Flew off to Alaska and was never seen again!

The Spotted Origami

The Spotted Origami
Is missing from its cage.
We think it could be hiding here –
Somewhere on this page.

Its tiny eyes – about the size
Of pinheads – are jet black.
Its feet are shaped like question marks
And leave an inky track.

It's paper-thin with snow-white skin.
Its spots are snow-white too.
If you should catch a glimpse of it,
Please telephone the zoo.

The digger's song

I'm a digger, a mechanical digger.
With my metal claws
I can scratch, I can scrape
Till I make the earth break.

I'm a digger, a mechanical digger.
With my metal jaws
I can bite, I can tear,
Ripping holes anywhere.

I'm a digger, a mechanical digger.
With my metal hands
I can scoop, I can lift.
Whole hills I can shift.

I'm a digger, a mechanical digger.
With my metal teeth
I can snatch, I can seize
Chunks of earth, roots of trees.

I'm a digger, a mechanical digger.
When there's work to be done,
Send for me! I'm the one
Who shifts earth by the ton!

Says of the week

Money-day. Pay away day.
Choose day. Whose day?
Wedding's day. Thick or thin day.
Furs day. Wrap up warm day.
Fries day. Hot dog day.
Sat-a-day. Armchair day.
Sons' day. Dads play.

The new gnus

A gnu who was new to the zoo
Asked another gnu what he should do.
The other gnu said, shaking his head,
'If I knew, I'd tell you, I'm new too!'

The llama

The llama is a charmer.
He'll take you by surprise.
He'll pull the wool
Over anyone's eyes.

Strange goings-on

Overnight,
The full-scale model of the Roman soldier,
Which was standing in the corner of the classroom,
Fell over.

When we arrived this morning,
He was lying sprawled across the floor,
As if he was unconscious.

Tracy said, 'He must have slipped.'
Naima said, 'Maybe he fainted.'
Jason said, 'He probably just got fed up
Of standing there. I know I would.'

Someone else said, 'Maybe it was the cleaner.
The cord of the vacuum cleaner
Got wrapped round his ankles
And he tripped up.'

Miss said, 'He must have been unstable.'
'Do you mean he got drunk?' asked Derek.

'I think a gust of wind blew him over,'
Said Ashley.

'Perhaps there was an intruder,'
Suggested Lina.

But the windows were shut tight.

I think someone – a British man or woman –
Must have crept up on him during the night
And knocked him out.
What else can explain that mark
Like a huge bruise on his left cheek
And the cut on his chin?

I am a pencil

I am
a pencil.
I have
the power
to make
words
and figures.
I can
make faces
and draw
pictures.
I like
compasses
and rulers,
but am
afraid
of rubbers.
Keep me
sharp
and I'll
serve you
well.
But do not
lean on
me
too hard
or I
might break
and

DO NOT
CHEW ME –
I don’t
like
the taste
of your
tongue
!

Writing and sums

When the teacher asks us to write,
The words dance in my head,
Weaving neat patterns,
Gliding into their places,
Before flowing down my pencil
In an orderly procession.
But . . .
When the teacher tells me to do sums,
The figures fly round my head,
Fluttering like birds
Trapped behind glass,
Before escaping down my pencil
In frightened confusion.

Numbers

1 is a tall man all alone;
a sentry standing to attention.
2 is a coatpeg with a tail.
3 is a torn leaf, fluttering on the page.
4 is a kite which has lost its string.
5 is an iron fish-hook.
6 is an earpiece left behind by a walkman.
7 is a broken arrow.
8 is an acrobat – one ball balancing on another.
9 is a ladle for serving soup.
10 is a knife lying beside an empty plate.

I am a full stop.

I am a full stop.
At my command,
sentences halt.
At its peril,
a letter which follows me
forgets it should be a capital.
I place myself between words.
I create meaning.
When children ignore me,
I cause confusion.
I am a full stop.
Learn to control *me*
and the whole written world
is yours.

Four o'clock Friday

Four o'clock Friday, I'm home at last,
Time to forget the week that's past.
On Monday, in break they stole my ball
And threw it over the playground wall.
On Tuesday aftcrnoon, in games
They threw mud at me and called me names.
On Wednesday, they trampled my books on the floor,
So Miss kept me in because I swore.
On Thursday, they laughed after the test
'Cause my marks were lower than the rest.
Four o'clock Friday, at last I'm free,
For two whole days they can't get at me.

Teachers!

Teachers!
I don't understand them.

They say:
When you hand in your work,
Make sure it's neat and tidy.
Then they mess it up
By scribbling illegible comments
All over it in red ink.

They say:
Don't interrupt when I'm talking.
Put your hand up
And wait until I've finished.
But if they've got something to say,
They clap their hands
And stop your discussions in mid-sentence.

They say:
Always plan your writing.
Take your time. Think it through
And do a rough draft.
Then they sit you in an examination hall
And ask you to write an essay
On one of six topics –
None of which interests you –
In an hour and a quarter.

They say:
All work and no play
Makes Jill a dull girl.
Make sure you allow yourself
Time off from your studies
To relax and enjoy yourself.
Then, when you don't hand
Your homework in on time,
Because you took their advice,
They keep you in after school.

Teachers!
I don't understand them.

Turning points

Yesterday
Our teacher
Told us the story
Of Lot's wife
Who looked back
And was turned
Into a pillar of salt.

'That's nothing,'
Said Tracy Saunders.
'My mum was backing the car
And when she looked round
She'd turned into a ditch!'

The double-decker bus

We like riding on the double-decker bus.
Up on the top deck that's the place for us!

In the front seat with the driver down below,
We give the orders, tell him where to go.

Tell him when to speed up, when to slow down.
We drive the double-decker right through town.

We drive it up the hill and park by the gate.
We make sure that the bus is never late.

We like riding on the double-decker bus.
The front seat on the top deck –
That's the place for us!

Holidays

Happy-go-lucky days.
Off out and about days.
Lazy lie-in-bed days.
In front of TV days.
Do as you please days.
Away to the sea days.
You can choose what to do days.
School's over! We're free days!

Recipe for a summer holiday

Take a stretch of sandy beach
And a calm sea.
Add a pier, a promenade,
donkey-rides and a fun-fair.
Sprinkle with buckets and spades,
deck-chairs, lilos and picnic-baskets.
Cover with thick slices of sunshine
And wrap in warm photographs
To look at on dark winter days.

Sand

Sand in your fingernails
Sand between your toes
Sand in your earholes
Sand up your nose!

Sand in your sandwiches
Sand on your bananas
Sand in your bed at night
Sand in your pyjamas!

Sand in your sandals
Sand in your hair
Sand in your knickers
Sand everywhere!

The smugglers

Through the sea-mist
Two small boats glide,
Slipping ashore
On the evening tide.

A man with a lantern
Flashes a light
To warn those on shore,
'We're coming tonight.'

A messenger hurries
From door to door,
Whispering softly,
'They're coming ashore.'

Down the cliff path
Six shadows glide
To the foot of the cliff
Where they crouch and hide.

They watch and wait,
Not saying a word,
Until the sound
Of the oars is heard.

Then, quickly, they hurry
Across the sand.
The barrels are passed
From hand to hand.

They are stacked in the cave
And hidden away
Till it's safe to move them
Another day.

Then, back to their beds
The shadows glide,
While the boats slip away
On the outgoing tide.

Football story

This is the foot.

This is the foot
That kicked the ball.

This is the foot
That kicked the ball
That scored the goal.

This is the foot
That kicked the ball
That scored the goal
That won the cup.

This is the foot
That kicked the ball
That scored the goal
That won the cup
The day that the final
Was played in our yard.

This is the ball.

This is the ball
That was kicked by the foot
That scored the goal
That won the cup
The day that the final
Was played in our yard.

This is the ball
That flew over the fence
When kicked by the foot
That scored the goal
That won the cup
The day that the final
Was played in our yard.

This is the ball
That flew over the fence
And smashed the window
Of next door's kitchen
When kicked by the foot
That scored the goal
That won the cup
The day that the final
Was played in our yard.

This is the boy.

This is the boy
Who ran away.

This is the boy
Who ran away
To hide in the shed
When he heard the crash
Made by the ball
That flew over the fence
And smashed the window
Of next door's kitchen

When kicked by the foot
That scored the goal
That won the cup
The day that the final
Was played in our yard.

This is the father.

This is the father
Who found the boy
Who ran away
To hide in the shed
When he heard the crash
Made by the ball
That flew over the fence
And smashed the window
Of next door's kitchen
When kicked by the foot
That scored the goal
That won the cup
The day that the final
Was played in our yard.

This is the father
Who dragged home the boy
Who ran away
When he heard the crash
Made by the ball
That flew over the fence
And smashed the window
Of next door's kitchen

When kicked by the foot
That scored the goal
That won the cup
The day that the final
Was played in our yard.

This is the hand.

This is the hand
Of the father
Who dragged home the boy
Who ran away
When he heard the crash
Made by the ball
That flew over the fence
And smashed the window
Of next door's kitchen
When kicked by the foot
That scored the goal
That won the cup
The day that the final
Was played in our yard.

This is the hand
Of the father
Who spanked the boy
Who ran away
When he heard the crash
Made by the ball
That flew over the fence
And smashed the window

Of next door's kitchen
When kicked by the foot
That scored the goal
That won the cup
The day that the final
Was played in our yard.

And this is the boy
Who can't sit down.

Mowers

Jim's dad has a motor mower.
He says it has a mind of its own.
It charges up and down their lawn
Snorting like an angry bull,
Flinging grass cuttings everywhere.

Mrs Spencer next door has an electric mower.
She bustles up and down her lawn,
Ironing it into neat, straight lines
Until there's not a blade of grass out of place.
Her lawn is as flat as a cricket pitch.

Grandad's got a hand-mower.
It rattles and clanks as he pushes it along.
It tears at the grass, chewing it up.
Grandad's lawn looks as if it's had a haircut
With a blunt pair of scissors.

Somehow it's not the same

On Sundays when we go to the park
We play a football game.
My step-dad always plays with me,
But somehow it's not the same.

Sometimes we'll go down the pond
To sail the models he's made.
But somehow it's not the same
As the games my dad and I played.

He takes me for burger and chips
And pays for my rides at the fair.
But somehow it's not the same
As it was when my dad took me there.

There are four chairs round the table

There are four chairs round the table,
Where we sit down for our tea.
But now we only set places
For Mum, for Terry and me.

We don't chatter any more
About what we did in the day.
Terry and I eat quickly,
Then we both go out to play.

Mum doesn't smile like she used to.
Often, she just sits and sighs.
Sometimes, I know from the smudges,
That while we are out she cries.

Parents!

Parents!
They're so embarrassing.

When my dad sneezes,
He makes such a racket
It's as if a minor explosion
Has been detonated
Inside his nose.
Then he whips out
His handkerchief with a flourish
And trumpets loudly,
Shattering the silence
With his coughing, spluttering and wheezing.

As for my mum,
Her stomach gurgles and rumbles
Like a broken cistern
That never stops filling.
It saves the loudest churnings
For that moment's silence
In the middle of a concert
Or the most dramatic moment
At the climax of a play,
So people turn and frown
Or pretend not to notice,
Though they couldn't help but have heard.
And I go bright red,
Wishing the ground would open up
And swallow me,

Or that I was cool and confident enough
To look disdainful,
As if to say:
She's not my mum, you know.
Don't blame me!

Parents!
They're so embarrassing.

Questions

Dad, why are you shaking me Dad?
Dad! It's the middle of the night.
I can't see to pack my things.
Why can't I switch on the light?

Dad, where are we going Dad?
Why do we have to go?
Dad, what's going on Dad?
I have a right to know.

Dad, why are you sighing Dad?
Dad, why are you lying?
That's not the real reason Dad.
Dad, why are you crying?

Early to bed

The thing I can't stand
About grown-ups
Is the way
They say
You can't stay up late
To watch TV.
They make you
Go off to bed
Then keep you awake
By watching themselves
Till it closes down,

While you're lying in bed
With the noise
Of the programmes
Drumming through your head.

Then, in the morning,
When you're yawning,
And they're being crabby
Because they're tired
From staying up too late,
They say:
There you are, you see,
You stayed up too late
Watching TV.
It's early to bed
For you tonight.
Then, they rush off to work
Thinking they're right.

No change

We've called in the telly repairman.
The channels won't change any more,
Since the dog chewed the channel controller
And spat out the bits on the floor.

Race you

Race you back to the flat.
Race you up those steps.
Race you across that bridge.
Race you down the hill.
My brother and I
Are always having races.
He always wins
Because he's three years older
And much bigger and faster than me.
The only time I ever won
Was when he said:
'Race you across the pond.'
Half-way across he slipped.
He fell on the ice
And broke his wrist.

When I said I'd won,
He said, 'You only won
Because I slipped and fell,
That doesn't count.'
'Of course it does,' I said,
'Doesn't it, Mum?'
But she said,
'You and your races.
If you hadn't been racing,
This would never have happened.
It's all your fault.'

Why is it
That even when he loses,
My brother always wins?

He wouldn't even let me sign his plaster,
Until I said
It didn't count.

The invaders

Today it is snowing.
The starlings are out in force
Bullying the sparrows,
Their bayonet beaks
Commandeering the breadcrumbs.
Like stormtroopers
They take over the garden,
Asserting that might means right.

Giant Winter

Giant Winter preys on the earth,
Gripping with talons of ice,
Squeezing, seeking a submission,
Tightening his grip like a vice.

Starved of sunlight, shivering trees
Are bent by his torturing breath.
The seeds burrow into the soil
Preparing to fight to the death.

Giant Winter sneers at their struggles,
Blows blizzards from his frozen jaws,
Ripples cold muscles of iron,
Clenches tighter his icicle claws.

Just as he seems to be winning,
Strength suddenly ebbs from his veins.
He releases his hold and collapses.
Giant Spring gently takes up the reins.

Snarling, bitter with resentment,
Winter crawls to his polar den,
Where he watches and waits till it's time
To renew the battle again.

Month by month

Jan you really are cold.
Feb you're even colder.
March with a spring in your step.
April has a smile on her face.
Maybe the sun will shine, maybe it won't.
D'you know it's meant to be summer!
D'you lie getting a suntan
Or gusts of spray in your face?
Sept-ember's glowing red cheeks.
Octo-burns the autumn leaves.
N-N-November's chillness.
Dis ember is flickering . . . stillness.

The old windmill

Like a sentinel
The old windmill
Stands guard
On the brow of the hill.

Stripped of their sails
The arthritic arms
Creak in the midsummer gales,
While the ghost of the miller
Grinds the corn.

When the wind blows

When the wind blows
Coats flap, scarves flutter.

When the wind blows
Branches groan, leaves mutter.

When the wind blows
Curtains swish, papers scatter.

When the wind blows
Gates creak, dustbins clatter.

When the wind blows
Doors slam, windows rattle.

When the wind blows
Inside is a haven,
Outside is a battle.

Winds

The spring wind
Is a bouncy breeze
Coaxing seeds and shoots,
Showering promises of summer.

The summer wind
Is a parched sigh
Rustling wheatfields,
Stirring up dust.

The autumn wind
Is a mischievous thief
Whistling cheerfully,
Scattering leaves with abandon.

The winter wind
Is an icicle wind
Knifing through bark,
Chilling to the bone.

The river

Some days
the river slips
so quietly under the bridge,
you can hardly tell
it's moving.

Other days
the river rushes
so quickly under the bridge
you wonder
what all the hurry is about.

The lake

On a calm day
The lake
Imagines it is a mirror
And smiles back
At people who pass by
Smiling.

On a breezy day
The lake
Hunches its shoulders
And sends ripples
Scudding across the surface.

On a winter's day
The lake
Hides itself
Under a frozen blanket
And refuses to budge
Until it is warm enough
To come out again.

Great-Gran

Great-Gran just sits
All day long there,
Beside the fire,
Propped in her chair.

Sometimes she mumbles
Or gives a shout,
But we can't tell
What it's about.

Great-Gran just sits
All day long there.
Her face is blank,
An empty stare.

When anyone speaks,
What does she hear?
When Great-Gran starts,
What does she fear?

How can we tell?
For we can't find
A key which can
Unlock her mind.

Great-Gran just sits,
Almost alone,
In some dream world
All of her own.

But when Mum bends
Tucking her rug
Perhaps she senses
That loving hug.

My Gramp

My Gramp has got a medal.
On the front there is a runner.
On the back it says:
Senior Boys 100 Yards
First William Green.
I asked him about it,
but before he could reply
Gran said, 'Don't listen to his tales.
The only running he ever did
was after the girls.'
Gramp gave a chuckle
and went out the back
to get the tea.
As he shuffled down the passage
with his back bent,
I tried to imagine him,
legs flying, chest out,
breasting the tape.
But I couldn't.

Gran

In winter Gran got chilblains.
Calling to see her
On the way home from school
I'd catch her with her skirt
Up round her knees,
Her feet immersed
In a white enamel bowl
Full of a steaming yellow liquid –
A mustard bath.

Gran's gone now.
Instead of mustard powder
We buy our mustard in pots
From the supermarket.
When I had chilblains,
The doctor gave me a prescription
For an ointment from the chemist.
As I rubbed it on
I thought of Gran,
The white enamel bowl,
The yellow liquid,
Her feet swollen and chapped,
Her mittened hands.

Just another war

On her sideboard
Nan has a picture
Of a young man
In a soldier's uniform
Smiling proudly.

'That's my brother,
Your Uncle Reg,'
She says,
Her voice tinged
With sadness.

'He was killed
In Korea.
He was only nineteen.'

'Where's Korea?' I say.
'What were they fighting for?'

'Somewhere in Asia,'
She says.
'I don't know.
It was just another war.'

War games

In a Star Wars T-shirt,
Armed with an Airfix bomber,
The young avenger
Crawls across the carpet
To blast the wastepaper basket
Into oblivion.

Later,
Curled on the sofa,
He watches unflinching
An edited version
Of War of the Day,
Only half-listening
As the newscaster
Lists the latest statistics.

Cushioned by distance
How can he comprehend
The real score?

WordSwordS

(A wargame)

Play with words.
Make a sword.
Shift gear
Into rage.
Turn snug
Into guns.
Make raw
Make war:
Listen – enlist
Tool – loot.
Roses
Becomes sores,
While skill
Kills.

It's raining cats and dogs

MUM: It's raining cats and dogs out there.

GRAN: The dog's out where?

MUM: No, it's raining very hard.
It's very wet out.

GRAN: The vet's come out.
Why? Is the dog not well?

MUM: The dog's fine.

GRAN: No, it's not.
It's raining cats and dogs.

Graveyard scene

There are no names on the gravestones now,
They've been washed away by the rain.
The graveyard trees are skeletons now,
They will never wear leaves again.

Instead of a forest, the tower surveys
A bleak and desolate plain.
Those are not tears in the gargoyle's eyes,
They are droplets of acid rain.

Pollution

P is for plastic that will not decay.
O for the oil slick that threatens the bay.
L for the lakes where the fish are all dead.
L for the dangerous levels of lead.
U for the uncontrolled dumping in seas.
T for the acid rain's threat to the trees.
I for increased CO_2 in the air.
O for the decreasing ozone layer.
N for the nuclear waste we must store
for thousands of years at sea or on shore.

Fox farm

The silver fox
with glossy fur,
penned in its man-made den,
paces the prison
yard of its cage,
again, again, again.

The farmer sneers:
'Why should I care?
I'm not breaking the law.'
The restless fox
prowls without point
a wire-mesh tundra floor.

The fashion-hounds,
dripping with scent,
admire and stroke his pelt.
The farmer shrugs,
pleads innocence,
stuffs banknotes in his belt.

Aunty Joan

When Aunty Joan became a phone,
She sat there not saying a thing.
The doctor said, shaking his head,
'You'll just have to give her a ring.'

We had a try, but got no reply.
The tone was always engaged.
'She's just being silly,' said Uncle Billy,
Slamming down the receiver enraged.

'Alas, I fear,' said the engineer,
Who was called in to inspect her.
'I've got no choice, she's lost her voice.
I shall have to disconnect her.'

The phone gave a ring. 'You'll do no such thing,'
Said Aunty's voice on the line.
'I like being a phone. Just leave me alone,
Or else I'll dial nine, nine, nine!'

Electric Fred

Electric Fred has wires in his head
And one hundred watt light bulbs for eyes,
Which means, of course, he can talk in morse
Or flash red, white and blue with surprise.

Just for a lark, he can shoot a spark
For three hundred feet out of his nose.
Wear rubber bands, if you shake his hands,
Or the current will tingle your toes.

Sometimes he chews a fifteen amp fuse,
Or recharges himself via the fire.
Just give him jolts of thousands of volts
And you'll find he's a really live wire!

Elastic Jones

Elastic Jones had rubber bones.
He could bounce up and down like a ball.
When he was six, one of his tricks
Was jumping a ten-foot wall.

As the years went by, Elastic would try
To jump higher, and higher, and higher.
He amazed people by jumping a steeple
Though he scratched his behind on the spire!

But, like many a star, he went too far,
Getting carried away with his power.
He boasted one day, 'Get out of my way,
I'm going to jump Blackpool Tower.'

He took off from near the end of the pier,
But he slipped and crashed into the top.
Amid cries and groans, Elastic Jones
Fell into the sea with a plop.

When Dracula went to the dentist

When Dracula went to the dentist,
The dentist smiled and said,
'There is nothing wrong with your teeth
Except for these specks of red.

'I wish that I had teeth like yours,'
Said the dentist brushing away.
'They're the finest set of teeth
I've seen for many a day.'

'You too can have a set like mine,'
Smiled Dracula. 'Here's my cheque.
Just pay it in at the blood bank
Along with that blood from your neck.'

The mad magician

In a dark and dingy dungeon
The Mad Magician dwells,
Mixing poisonous potions,
Concocting evil spells.

Into his bubbling cauldron
The Mad Magician throws
Handfuls of wriggling maggots,
The eyes of two dead crows.

The bladder of a nanny goat,
The snout of a year old pig,
An eagle's claw, a vampire's tooth,
Hairs plucked from a judge's wig.

He waves his wicked wizard's wand.
He utters a piercing cry.
From their lairs, deep in the earth,
A thousand demons fly.

In a dark and dingy dungeon
The Mad Magician dwells,
Mixing poisonous potions,
Concocting evil spells.

Colour story – from gold to silver

Gold is a blaring trumpet call.
Blue is a shivering stream.
Yellow is a tickle of laughter.
White is the whistling dream.

Red is a scream, a strangled cry.
Orange is the spluttering flames.
Grey is the murmuring mist.
Silver is the rattle of chains.

The hour when the witches fly

When the night is as cold as stone,
When lightning severs the sky,
When your blood is chilled to the bone,
That's the hour when the witches fly.

When the night-owl swoops for the kill,
When there's death in the fox's eye,
When the snake is coiled and still,
That's the hour when the witches fly.

When the nightmares scream in your head,
When you hear a strangled cry,
When you startle awake in your bed,
That's the hour when the witches fly.

When the sweat collects on your brow,
When the minutes tick slowly by,
When you wish it was then not now,
That's the hour when the witches fly.

The shadow man

At night-time
As I climb the stair
I tell myself
There's nobody there.

But what if there is?
What if he's there –
The Shadow Man
At the top of the stair.

What if he's lurking
There in the gloom
Of the landing
Right outside my room?

The Shadow Man
Who's so hard to see.
What if he's up there
Waiting for me?

At night-time
As I climb the stair
I tell myself
There's nobody there.

The central heating

There's a monster haunts our house –
It's called the central heating.
From the way its stomach rumbles,
Goodness knows what it's been eating!

It wakes us up at night-time
With its gurglings and its groanings,
Its clattering and its clanging,
Its mutterings and moanings.

Mum says it lives on water,
In answer to my question.
I think that it must gulp it down
To get such indigestion!

Why is it?

Why is it
That when we go to the park
to fly my kite
the string always gets tangled
in the trees
and the kite gets torn,
while other kids' kites
go soaring and swooping?

Why is it
that when we play cricket
on the beach
my dad always drops catches
and is out first ball,
while other kids' dads
hit the ball
over the breakwater
into the sea?

Why is it
that when my mum asks my dad
to put up a picture
on the wall,
he drills a hole

that's far too big
and gets plaster everywhere?

But when my dad
tells my brother and me stories
in the dark,
Why is it
I can almost see
the creatures
and feel their hot breath?